D0492622

9112000380251

Raintree is an imprint of Capstone Global
Library Limited, a company incorporated in
England and Wales having its registered office
at 264 Banbury Road, Oxford, OX2 7DY –
Registered company number: 6695582

www.raintree.co.uk
myorders@raintree.co.uk

Copyright © 2019 DC Comics.
Originally published by DC Comics in
SUPER POWERS #5 Copyright © 2017
All Rights Reserved. All characters, their distinctive
likenesses and related elements featured in this
publication are trademarks of DC Comics. The
stories, characters and incidents featured in this
publication are entirely fictional.

No part of this publication may be produced in
whole or in part, or stored in a retrieval system,
or transmitted in any form or by any means,
electronic, mechanical, photocopying, recording,
or otherwise, without written permissions of the
publisher.

ISBN 978 1 4747 6664 7
22 21 20 19 18
10 9 8 7 6 5 4 3 2 1

British Library Cataloguing in Publication Data
A full catalogue record for this book is available
from the British Library

Editorial: Chris Harbo and Gena Chester
Design: Hilary Wacholz
Production: Kris Wilfahrt
Originated by Capstone Global Library Ltd
Printed and bound in India

Superman created by Jerry Siegel and Joe
Shuster. By special arrangement with the
Jerry Siegel family.

BRENT LIBRARIES	
KIN	
91120000380251	
Askews & Holts	05-Sep-2018
JF PIC BOOK OLDER	£5.99

SUPER POWERS!

Pryme Time!

BY ART BALTAZAR AND FRANCO

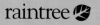

raintree

a Capstone company — publishers for children

6

9

18

CREATORS

ART BALTAZAR IS A CARTOONIST MACHINE FROM THE HEART OF CHICAGO! HE DEFINES CARTOONS AND COMICS NOT ONLY AS AN ART STYLE, BUT AS A WAY OF LIFE. CURRENTLY, ART IS THE CREATIVE FORCE BEHIND *THE NEW YORK TIMES* BEST-SELLING, EISNER AWARD-WINNING DC COMICS SERIES TINY TITANS, THE CO-WRITER FOR *BILLY BATSON AND THE MAGIC OF SHAZAM!*, AND CO-CREATOR OF SUPERMAN FAMILY ADVENTURES. ART IS LIVING THE DREAM! HE DRAWS COMICS AND NEVER HAS TO LEAVE THE HOUSE. HE LIVES WITH HIS LOVELY WIFE, ROSE, BIG BOY SONNY, LITTLE BOY GORDON AND LITTLE GIRL AUDREY. RIGHT ON!

ART BALTAZAR

FRANCO

FRANCO AURELIANI, BRONX, NEW YORK, BORN WRITER AND ARTIST, HAS BEEN DRAWING COMICS SINCE HE COULD HOLD A CRAYON. CURRENTLY RESIDING IN UPSTATE NEW YORK WITH HIS WIFE, IVETTE, AND SON, NICOLAS, FRANCO SPENDS MOST OF HIS DAYS IN A BATCAVE-LIKE STUDIO WHERE HE HAS PRODUCED DC'S TINY TITANS COMICS. IN 1995, FRANCO FOUNDED BLINDWOLF STUDIOS, AN INDEPENDENT ART STUDIO WHERE HE AND FELLOW CREATORS CAN CREATE CHILDREN'S COMICS. FRANCO IS THE CREATOR, ARTIST, AND WRITER OF *PATRICK THE WOLF BOY*. WHEN HE'S NOT WRITING AND DRAWING, FRANCO ALSO TEACHES HIGH SCHOOL ART.

GLOSSARY

apprentice someone who learns a trade by working with a skilled person

command have control over something, or to give an order

demon evil creature or spirit

fiend evil or cruel person

formally officially and properly

fragment piece or part that has broken from a larger whole

heroic very brave or daring

hilarious very funny

influence have an effect on someone or something

lair villain's hideout

modification change to the original plan or condition

pharaoh name given to the rulers of ancient Egypt

treachery break a trust with someone else

upgrade improve something

VISUAL QUESTIONS AND WRITING PROMPTS

1. OTHER THAN BRAINIAC, WHAT ELSE COULD LEX LUTHOR CONTROL WITH THE CRYSTALS?

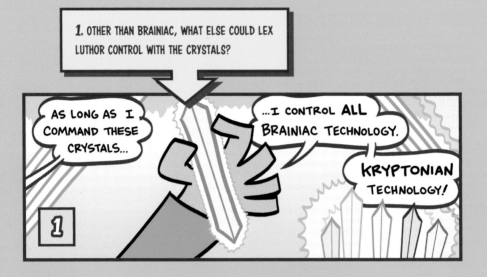

2. THE JOKER IS GOTHAM CITY'S WORST VILLAIN. WHY DO YOU THINK COMMISSIONER GORDON LETS HIM GO?

3. LOOK AT THE PANEL BELOW. WHICH SHADOWS BELONG TO WHICH CHARACTERS? HOW CAN YOU TELL?

4. WHAT ARE THE DIFFERENCES BETWEEN FUTURE PRYM-EL AND PRESENT PRYM-EL?

READ THEM ALL!

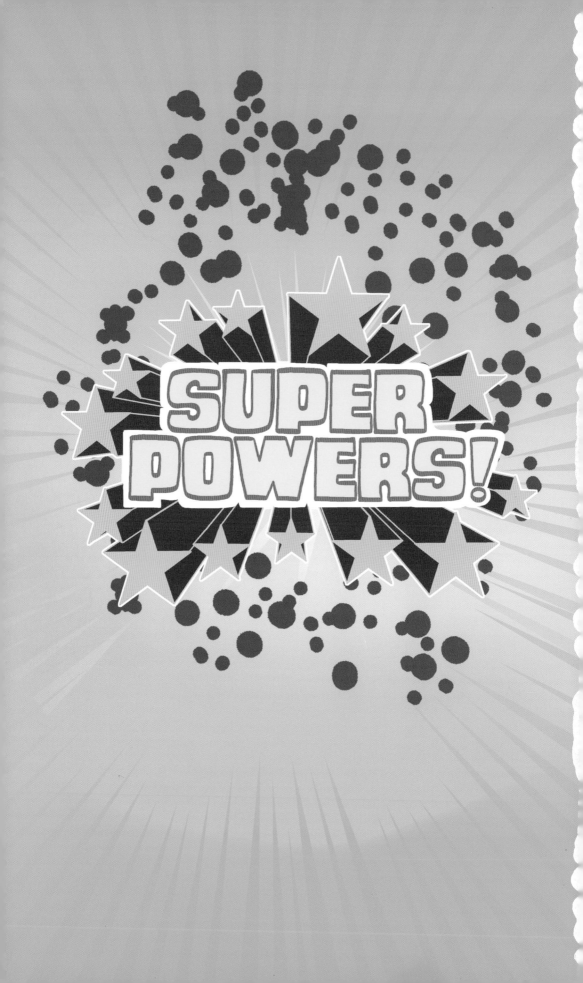